Withdrawn

Boffin Boy Goes to Hollywood
by David Orme

Illustrated by Peter Richardson

Published by Ransom Publishing Ltd.
Radley House, 8 St Cross Road, Winchester, Hants. SO23 9HX
www.ransom.co.uk

ISBN   978 178127 046 2
First published in 2013
Reprinted 2014
Copyright © 2013 Ransom Publishing Ltd.

Illustrations copyright © 2013 Peter Richardson

A CIP catalogue record of this book is available from the British
Library.

Design & layout: *redpaperdesign.co.uk*

Find out more about Boffin Boy at *www.ransom.co.uk*.

Boffin Boy
GOES TO
HOLLYWOOD

By David Orme

Illustrated by Peter Richardson

The superheroes are arriving in Hollywood …

The world's superheroes are all there ...

... except Boffin Boy.

Much later, outside the Wizard of Edo's secret hideout …

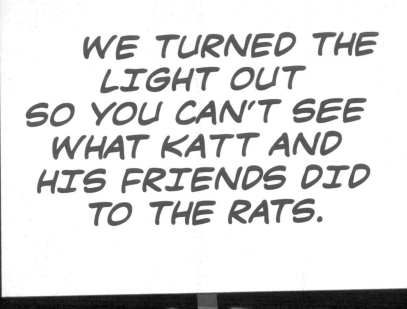

WE TURNED THE
LIGHT OUT
SO YOU CAN'T SEE
WHAT KATT AND
HIS FRIENDS DID
TO THE RATS.

ABOUT THE AUTHOR

David Orme has written well over 200 books including poetry collections, fiction and non-fiction, and school text books. He especially likes writing science fiction stories, and historical stories set in London. Find out more at: www.magic-nation.com.